Hodder Gibson

Scottish Examination M

HIGHER
BIOLOGY
Key Terms

John Di Mambro
B.Sc., B.A., M.A., Dip.Ed.Tech., C.Biol., F.I.Biol.

Hutchesons' Grammar School

Hodder Gibson
2A Christie Street, Paisley, PA1 1NB

Orders: please contact Bookpoint Ltd, 130 Milton Park, Abingdon, Oxon OX14 4SB. Telephone: (44) 01235 827720. Fax: (44) 01235 400454. Lines are open from 9.00–6.00, Monday to Saturday, with a 24 hour message answering service. You can also order through our website www.hodderheadline.co.uk.

British Library Cataloguing in Publication Data
A catalogue record for this title is available from the British Library

ISBN 0 340 813113

Published by Hodder Gibson, 2a Christie Street, Paisley PA1 1NB.
Tel: 0141 848 1609; Fax: 0141 889 6315; Email: hoddergibson@hodder.co.uk
First Published 2004
Impression number   10 9 8 7 6 5 4 3 2 1
Year   2010 2009 2008 2007 2006 2005 2004

Typeset by Fakenham Photosetting Limited, Fakenham, Norfolk
Printed in Great Britain for Hodder Gibson, 2a Christie Street, Paisley, PA1 1NB, Scotland, UK

PREFACE

It has been said that Biologists never use a short word if a longer one will do! A major obstacle for students is often just understanding the specialist vocabulary, frequently derived from Latin and Greek, which surrounds Biology, making it sometimes difficult to read through material. A term such as 'daughter' will seem very familiar in everyday speech but when used biologically to describe the new cells produced after normal cell division, it carries a quite different and specific meaning. In other words, the terms are often context-related. With this in mind, a need was felt to produce a suitable and comprehensive list of key terms for students at school and college taking Higher Biology. This list has been designed specifically to link with all of the three main topics: Cell Biology, Genetics and Adaptation, and Growth and Regulation. The design is intended to be as user-friendly as possible, the key terms being arranged alphabetically making them easy and quick to look up. The definitions are all set within the limited context of the course so that, in almost all cases, while they are certainly not exhaustive, they are nevertheless sufficient to satisfy the course requirement. For example, a term such as 'induction' has considerably more meanings than those offered here but it was not appropriate to include these.

The use of this material can form a powerful tool to aid revision in two different ways. Firstly, a student could be presented with a selection of the terms and asked to generate a suitable definition for each, and secondly, given the definition, the student has to supply the appropriate key term. This kind of exercise, employing a questioner and responder, can benefit two people at once. If this were done for all these terms, it would be a very transparent index of how effectively the student has revised the course to-date prior to the National Examination. Failure to achieve either of these two operations for any key term should immediately direct the student to search out the relevant part of the course and revise it more rigorously.

Learning terms, particularly unusual scientific ones, can be tedious and there is no suggestion that students should attempt to learn by rote these definitions. It is better that the meanings of the key terms 'osmose' naturally as the student progresses through the theory so that the explanations are in context. These definitions are not definitive in the sense that students can use alternatives providing they maintain the same general meaning and that is also a good exercise for revision, trying to explain the key term in one's own words.

KEYWORD	DEFINITION
A	
ABSCISSION	A general term for the process of shedding plant parts such as ripe fruits and deciduous leaves.
ABSORBED LIGHT	Light that has been taken in by a leaf, some of which will be used in photosynthesis, the rest being lost to the environment as heat.
ABSORPTION	The process by which small, soluble molecules such as glucose are taken up by cells from their environment.
ABSORPTION SPECTRUM	A graphical representation of the amount of light of different wavelengths taken in by a pigment such as chlorophyll a.
ACCESSORY PIGMENT	A plant pigment that can absorb additional wavelengths of light not taken in by the main pigment chlorophyll.
ACETYL COENZYME A	Important metabolite containing a 2-carbon molecule found in the krebs cycle.
ACQUIRED IMMUNE DEFICIENCY SYNDROME	A disease caused by the retrovirus human immunodeficiency virus (HIV), which targets the immune system. The affected person is therefore at an increased risk of developing a range of infections and/or cancer.
ACQUIRED IMMUNITY	Immunity obtained after exposure to an antigen.
ACROMEGALY	A condition caused by an over-production of growth hormone in adults producing increased sizes of feet, hands, facial bones, tongue and ribs.
ACTIN	A globular protein found in muscle tissue which takes part in muscular contraction.
ACTION SPECTRUM	A graphical representation of the relationship between the light absorbed and the level of photosynthetic activity.
ACTIVATOR	A small molecule that can bind to an enzyme, thereby increasing its activity.
ACTIVE IMMUNITY	A defence mechanism by which the host produces antibodies to a foreign antigen.
ACTIVE SITE	An area on an enzyme's surface that binds with a specific substrate.

KEYWORD	DEFINITION
ACTIVE TRANSPORT	An energy-requiring process in cells that moves substances against a concentration gradient.
ACYANOGENIC	The inability of a plant to produce the poison cyanide.
ADAPTATION	The process by which an organism is best suited to its environment as a result of natural selection over a long period of time.
ADAPTIVE RADIATION	An evolutionary process by which a particular species spreads into new habitats and exploits new resources. Over a period of time, these groups may become new species. It is sometimes called divergent evolution.
ADENINE	One of the five bases that form nucleotides of nucleic acids.
ADENOSINE DIPHOSPHATE	A molecule consisting of the nucleotide adenosine and two phosphate groups which can be formed by the hydrolysis of adenosine triphosphate (ATP); abbreviated ADP.
ADENOSINE TRIPHOSPHATE	A molecule consisting of the nucleotide adenosine and three phosphate groups; abbreviated ATP. It is the main energy carrier molecule found in all living things.
ADHESION	A force that tends to make liquids stick to the surfaces within which they are contained.
ADRENAL GLAND	An endocrine gland that secretes several important hormones, including adrenaline and noradrenaline.
ADRENALINE	A hormone secreted by the adrenal glands, which are situated above the kidneys. It increases the ability of the body to deal with stressful situations, a response known as the "fight or flight" reaction.
ADVENTITIOUS ROOT	A root that is growing from the stem area of a plant instead of the normal main root.
AEROBIC RESPIRATION	A type of respiration requiring oxygen in which substrates such as glucose are completely oxidised to water and carbon dioxide to release large amounts of energy.
AGGLUTINATION	The clumping of cells caused by a reaction between cell surface antigens and antibodies to form visible precipitates.
AGRICULTURE	The cultivation of land to raise crops, domestic animals etc. to provide food and other products useful to humans.

KEYWORD	DEFINITION
ALBINISM	A genetically determined inborn error of metabolism in which none of the pigment melanin is found in the hair, skin, eyes etc. Affected individuals are homozyous for the defective recessive allele. The dominant normal allele codes for the enzyme tyrosinase, which is required for the synthesis of melanin.
ALEURONE LAYER	A layer of cells found just below the protective outer covering of some seeds such as barley which contains enzymes that can convert the stored food and make it available to the developing embryo plant.
ALGA	A simple, one-celled or many-celled plant found mostly in water which uses sunlight to produce its own food. Algae can cause problems if they multiply in an uncontrolled way in lakes, lochs, reservoirs etc.
ALGAL BLOOM	An excess of algae often associated with an increase in the nutrient level in water.
ALLELE	One of two or more different forms of a gene. A plant or animal can carry only two alleles for each gene. Each allele is carried at similar positions on two homologous chromosomes.
ALPHA-AMYLASE	An enzyme found in the aleurone layer of some seeds which converts stored starch in the endosperm into sugar to be used by the embryo plant.
ALVEOLUS	A blind-ending, thin-walled air sac found in the lungs where gas exchange takes place.
AMINO ACID	A water-soluble molecule that is the basic building block of proteins. It is made up of the elements carbon, hydrogen, oxygen and nitrogen. Approximately 20 different amino acids are commonly found in proteins.
AMOEBA	A simple, single-celled organism often found in ponds.
ANAEMIA	A reduction in the haemoglobin content of the blood which can have various causes. It renders the person easily tired and prone to infections.
ANAEROBE	An organism that can survive in the absence of oxygen.
ANAEROBIC RESPIRATION	A type of respiration that does not require oxygen in which substrates such as glucose are partially broken down to lactic acid, releasing only small amounts of energy or alcohol.

KEYWORD	DEFINITION
ANGIOSPERM	A group of highly advanced plants that includes all those that flower. The reproductive organs are all found within the flower and the seeds formed are enclosed within fruits.
ANNUAL RING	Found within the woody stem of trees, giving an approximate indication of the tree's age. Each ring is usually formed within 1 year by alternate production of spring and autumn wood.
ANTAGONISM	Having the opposite effect to another agent, for example the negative effect of one hormone on the secretion of another or the opposite action of skeletal muscle pairs.
ANTHER	The male structure of a flower which contains the pollen grains.
ANTIBIOTIC	A chemical produced by a microorganism such as fungus or synthesised chemically, used to kill or inhibit the growth of pathogens which are sensitive to that chemical without damaging the host.
ANTIBODY	A large, globular protein molecule produced by B lymphocytes in response to exposure to a specific antigen. An antibody is capable of attacking that antigen and normally rendering it harmless.
ANTICODON	A sequence of three bases found on a transfer ribonucleic acid (tRNA) molecule which exactly complement a codon in a messenger ribonucleic acid (mRNA) molecule.
ANTIDIURETIC HORMONE	A hormone manufactured in the pituitary gland which regulates the blood water concentration in a number of ways, including increasing the permeability of the kidney tubules. This has the effect of causing more water to be reabsorbed and thus less to be passed out in the urine.
ANTIGEN	A complex protein or carbohydrate molecule that can provoke the immune response if that antigen is foreign to the host.
ANTIGENIC MARKER	A protein on the surface of a cell which identifies it as belonging to the host organism. It may form the basis of blood grouping for example.
ANTITOXIN	A special type of antibody produced in response to a poison, called a toxin, produced by a microorganism such as a bacterium or from some other source.
APE	The general term for a primate mammal that is tailless, including gorillas, chimpanzees, gibbons and orang-utans.

KEYWORD	DEFINITION
APICAL DOMINANCE	In plants, inhibition of the production of side shoots by means of hormones secreted by the bud at the top of the stem.
APICAL MERISTEM	The region of actively dividing cells at the tip of the stem or root.
ARTERIOLE	A small division of an artery.
ARTERY	The general term for a blood vessel that carries blood away from the heart towards the organs and other parts of the body.
ARTIFICIAL IMMUNITY	Immunity conferred by exposure to an antigen other than naturally, for example, by vaccination.
ARTIFICIAL INSEMINATION	Introducing sperm into the female reproductive tract of an animal by means other than natural.
ARTIFICIAL SELECTION	Deliberate choosing by humans of animals or plants for reproduction to obtain desirable features. Domestication of animals is an example.
ASEXUAL REPRODUCTION	Reproduction that does not involve the production of gametes such as sperm and eggs. In plants it is also known as vegetative reproduction.
ATMOMETER	The apparatus used to demonstrate the evaporation of water due to a non-biological process.
AUGER	An instrument that can bore holes in the earth or in wood.
AUTOSOME	A chromosome other than a sex chromosome.
AUTOTROPHIC NUTRITION	Feeding based on the manufacture of the necessary organic materials by the organism itself. Photosynthesis is an example of this type of nutrition.
AUTUMN WOOD	Wood formed in the later part of the summer which contains small and very thick walled vessels.
AUXIN	A plant growth substance whose effect is very much dependent on its concentration. Generally auxins will promote the elongation of cells and cell division. A well-known example is indole acetic acid (IAA).
AVOIDANCE BEHAVIOUR	A pattern of behaviour that is usually genetically based by which an animal minimises potential dangers. An animal may use vivid warning colours, strong smells, running away etc.

KEYWORD	DEFINITION
AXON	The long process of a nerve cell which carries information away from the area of the cell where the nucleus is located.

B

KEYWORD	DEFINITION
BACTERIOPHAGE	A virus that specifically attacks bacteria such as *Escherichia coli*.
BACTERIUM	A microscopic, unicellular organism, lacking a definite nuclear membrane, usually having a definite cell wall and which usually reproduces by simple binary fission. Bacteria range in size from 0.5 to 5 μm.
BARK	The outermost living layer in a tree.
BASE	A water-soluble chemical such as adenine, thymine, cytosine, guanine or uracil that contains the element nitrogen.
BASE PAIRING	The linking of complementary bases by hydrogen bonding.
BEHAVIOUR	An umbrella term for all or some of the observable patterns of activities, responses, movements etc.
BENEDICT'S REAGENT	A test for the presence of a reducing sugar. When the reagent is heated with a reducing sugar, a brick-red precipitate is formed and the original blue colour is lost.
BETA-GALACTOSIDASE	An enzyme that can break down lactose to galactose and glucose.
BICONCAVE	Being curved inwards on both sides such as is the case in a red blood cell.
BILE	A slightly viscous, dark-green liquid secreted by the liver and stored in the gall bladder. It consists of bile salts, bile pigments and other chemicals that help in the breakdown and ultimate absorption of fats.
BILE DUCT	The tube that carries bile, produced in the liver and stored in the gall bladder, to the duodenum.
BILE SALTS	A chemical mix that causes emulsification of fats in the duodenum.
BINARY FISSION	A simple type of reproduction where one cell divides into two identical new cells.

KEYWORD	DEFINITION
BIODEGRADABLE	Able to be naturally broken down, usually by the action of decomposers such as fungi and bacteria.
BIODIVERSITY	All the different species in a particular environment.
BIOMASS	The total mass of living things in the environment, usually expressed as the dry mass.
BIRTH CONTROL	Any strategy that prevents a pregnancy developing.
BIRTH RATE	A measure of the average number of animals born in a given time.
BLOOD	A transport fluid essential for life that contains many dissolved substances as well as floating cells. The average human male body contains around 5 litres of blood.
BLOOD VESSEL	The generalised term for any tube that carries blood.
BONE MARROW	The tissue found inside bones within which blood cells are manufactured.
BOUNDARY	The junction between two or more territorial areas in an environment.
BRAIN	A complex mass of nerve cells located within the skull where all the higher activities such as memory and judgement as well as lower activities such as regulating temperature are located.
BRONCHIOLE	A small division of the air passages that are found deep in the lungs.
BUSHY STUNT DISEASE	A disease of tomato and parsley plants caused by a ribonculeic acid (RNA) virus.

C	
CALCICOLE PLANT	A plant that thrives in an environment that is rich in calcium.
CALCIFUGE PLANT	A plant that does not tolerate high levels of calcium in the environment.
CALLUS	In plants, a collection of cells that form over a wound.
CALVIN CYCLE	A series of linked reactions that form part of the light-independent stage of photosynthesis. Carbon dioxide is fixed and reduced to glucose.

KEYWORD	DEFINITION
CAMBIUM	A group of actively dividing cells that cause the plant to grow laterally. Cambium is found between xylem and phloem.
CAMOUFLAGE	A strategy employed by organisms to disguise or hide themselves from a potential threat. It may employ the use of the colour, texture, etc. of the natural surroundings.
CAPILLARITY	The physical process that occurs in tubes of very small diameter by which liquids contained in them rise naturally; found for example in xylem vessels of plants.
CAPILLARY	The smallest-diameter blood vessel, whose walls are only one cell thick. Red blood cells are forced to pass through capillaries in single file. Only within capillary networks can exchange of gases and nutrients take place effectively.
CAPSID	The protein covering of a virus that protects the nucleic acid inside.
CARBOHYDRATE	A chemical that contains the elements carbon, hydrogen and oxygen in the general formula $(CH_2O)n$
CARBON CYCLE	The natural recirculation of carbon by the living processes of plants and animals, by respiration, photosynthesis, decompositon etc.
CARBON FIXATION	The conversion of the gas carbon dioxide by photosynthetic plants to produce glucose; sometimes referred to as the Calvin cycle.
CARBON MONOXIDE	A highly poisonous gas that is formed in the burning of some fuels. It can compete with oxygen for the haemoglobin molecule to form a stable compound which effectively permanently blocks the haemoglobin from combining with oxygen.
CAROTENE	Any of the several orange or yellow accessory pigments found in plants.
CARRIER	A person who is heterozygous for a gene so that they do not show any of the effects of the defective recessive allele, because they have a dominant normal allele. However, these individuals can pass the defective allele on to their offspring. If the gene is located on the X-chromosome, women can be carriers while men can not.
CARRIER MOLECULE	A molecule that is soluble in lipid and which can transport other molecules across the plasma membrane, a process which requires energy.

KEYWORD	DEFINITION
CARRYING CAPACITY	With reference to a habitat, the maximum number of any one species that can be sustained over time.
CASH CROP	A plant specifically grown for the income its sale will provide such as coffee, tea etc.
CATALASE	The fastest-acting enzyme currently known, which breaks down the powerful oxidising agent hydrogen peroxide as soon as it is formed.
CATALYST	A substance that can alter the rate of a reaction without itself being altered by that reaction. Enzymes are natural catalysts, found in all living cells.
CATECHOL OXIDASE	An enzyme found in plants such as potato and apple which will cause browning if the outer peel is removed.
CELL	The basic unit of life.
CELL MEMBRANE	The outer boundary of a cell, sometimes called the plasma membrane.
CELL SAP	The watery contents of the large vacuole found in many plant cells.
CELL WALL	The relatively thick layer found on the outside of plant, fungal and bacterial cells. In each case, it is chemically different but functions to give the cell shape and help protect internal cell structures.
CELLULASE	An enzyme that is capable of digesting cellulose into glucose.
CELLULOSE	The main structural polysaccharide that makes up plant cell walls.
CENTRIOLE	Either of two small, cylindrical structures, found near the nucleus at right angles to each other, which have an important role in forming the spindle.
CENTROMERE	The area of a chromosome where the daughter chromatids are held together. It is also the point to which spindle fibres become attached during cell division.
CHEMORECEPTOR	A group of specialised cells that can detect the presence or absence of a particular chemical. The taste buds are examples of chemoreceptors.
CHIASMA	The point where chromatids join during crossing over. Each chiasma indicates a cross-over event.

KEYWORD	DEFINITION
CHLORIDE SECRETORY CELL	A cell found in the gills of certain fish which has the ability to actively take in chloride ions from the water as it passes through the gills.
CHLOROFLUOROCARBON	A class of chemicals previously widely used as propellents in aerosols. Although chemically inert, when they reach the upper atmosphere they break down, releasing highly reactive chlorine molecules which then damage the ozone layer.
CHLOROPHYLL	The general term for the green pigment which traps solar radiation (mainly blue and red wavelengths) to be used in photosynthesis. There are several different types of chlorophyll molecules such as chlorophyll a and chlorophyll b.
CHLOROPLAST	A structure found in green plants which contains the pigment chlorophyll. It is the site of photosynthesis.
CHLOROSIS	A yellow appearance of plant tissue due to lack of chlorophyll.
CHROMATID	One of the two identical strands forming a chromosome held together by the centromere.
CHROMATOGRAM	The result of running a solvent through a pigment, usually on special paper.
CHROMATOGRAPHY	The technique of separating individual components from a mixture which will move with the solvent at different rates.
CHROMOPLAST	A coloured structure in plant cells which does not contain chlorophyll but usually some other pigment, which may be red or yellow.
CHROMOSOME	A thread-like structure composed of deoxyribonucleic acid (DNA) and other chemicals; found in the cell nucleus and çarrying genes. Humans have two copies of each chromosome, with 46 chromosomes altogether.
CHROMOSOME BAND	The dark region of a chromosome shown by the use of special staining technques. The banding pattern is consistent for a particular chromosome.
CHROMOSOME MAP	A description of the sequence of the genes on a chromosome.

KEYWORD	DEFINITION
CHROMOSOME MUTATION	A large-scale change in the structure and/or number of chromosomes. Most of these are lethal, because the organism cannot cope with the loss or gain of so much genetic information.
CILIUM	A small, threadlike structure that extends from the surface of some cells which line body parts, such as the respiratory system, and can move in a rhythmic and co-ordinated way.
CITRIC ACID	A six-carbon intermediate in the Krebs cycle.
CITRIC ACID CYCLE	A cyclical series of biochemical reactions operating under aerobic conditions and which occur in the mitochondrial matrix.
CLIMATE	The collective name for all the variable environmental factors affecting a particular place, usually considered over a long period of time. Climate will include rainfall, temperature, humidity, sunlight, atmospheric pressure etc.
CLIMAX COMMUNITY	An assembly of plants and animals that has reached a stable equilibrium with the environment as a result of a number of ecological successions which have now ceased.
CLINISTIX	A commercially available reagent to test for the presence of glucose by developing a purple-blue colour.
CLONE	A group of genetically identical cells or organisms.
CODON	A triplet of bases in deoxyribonucleic acid (DNA) or ribonucleic acid (RNA) which codes for a specific amino acid.
COENZYME	A small, non-protein molecule that temporarily associates with an enzyme molecule allowing the catalysis of a reaction but, like the enzyme itself, is not used up in the reaction. Some vitamins can act as coenzymes.
COHESION	The force of attraction between molecules which makes them stick together.
COLEOPTILE	The semi-transparent, protective covering found over the developing shoots of young plants.
COLLAGEN	An insoluble, fibrous structural protein that is the main chemical component of tendons. It is also found in bone, skin, cartilage and ligaments and is not very elastic.

KEYWORD	DEFINITION
COLOUR BLINDNESS	The genetically based inability to distinguish colours. The most common form is red-green colour blindness due to a recessive mutant allele carried on the X-chromosome.
COMBUSTION	A chemical process in which a substance, often a fuel, is combined with oxygen to release heat, light, sound and other chemical by-products.
COMMUNITY	A collection of animals and plants living together in a particular habitat.
COMPANION CELL	A cell which possesses many mitochondria and has a nucleus which help regulate translocation in the phloem. Companion cells are linked to phloem by strands of cytoplasm.
COMPENSATION POINT	A light intensity at which photosynthesis and respiration are in balance with each other. There is therefore no net gain or loss of carbon dioxide at this time.
COMPETITION	The interaction between living things for the same resources in their shared environment. Such resources include water, light, nutrients and space.
COMPETITIVE EXCLUSION PRINCIPLE	When two different species require the same environmental niche, only one will survive.
CONCENTRATION GRADIENT	The change in the concentration of ions or molecules, usually from one area to another.
CONJUGATED PROTEIN	A globular protein that has a non-protein component attachment. Haemoglobin is a conjugated protein that contains iron.
CONJUGATION	In bacteria, this refers to a process that is similar to sexual reproduction by which genetic material can be exchanged.
CONSERVATION	The action taken by humans to maintain their environment such as in the prevention of pollution or destruction of endangered animals or plants or sensitive areas of land such as tropical rainforests.
CONTINENTAL DRIFT	The movement of land masses on the Earth's surface over a long period of time. It has been suggested that originally the Earth's continents were a single structure.
CONTINUOUS VARIATION	The continual spread across a sample of a population for variables such as height, weight and surface area which are often controlled by a number of factors.

KEYWORD	DEFINITION
CONTOUR	An imaginary line on a map which shows some property of the land such as the relative height of that land to areas above and below it.
CONTRACTILE VACUOLE	A membrane-bound space in a cell which can fill with materials from the cell and empty its contents to the outside. It can therefore be used to regulate water balance and to excrete waste materials.
CONVERGENT EVOLUTION	When two or more unrelated organisms show the same features that have arisen by different evolutionary processes rather than from a common ancestor; for example, the wings of bats and insects.
CO-OPERATIVE HUNTING	Animal behaviour by which the common task of obtaining food is shared by a group of individuals; for example, the hunting behaviour of wild dogs.
CORK	The layer of dead, protective cells which forms in plants under the epidermis.
CORRELATION	A measure used in statistics for linking two or more variables such that a change in one will produce a predictable increase or decrease in the other(s). A high correlation suggests a linear relationship.
CORTEX	A general term for the outer part of any organ.
CRISTA	A fold in the inner membrane of a mitochondrion on which the electron transport system is located.
CROSSING OVER	A process occurring in meiosis whereby homologous chromosomes exchange sections of the chromatids, giving rise to recombination and thereby increasing variation.
CROSSOVER FREQUENCY	A measure of the percentage of gametes which possess a new combination of genetic material due to crossing over compared with the total number of offspring.
CROSS-POLLINATION	The transfer of pollen from one flower to another which may or may not be of the same species.
CULLING	The selecting and deliberate killing of individual animals in a population, e.g. hedgehogs, seals, deer, because they may be causing environmental damage or competing with an endangered species for resources etc.
CUTICLE	In plants, the continuous waxy layer that covers the surfaces exposed to the air.

KEYWORD	DEFINITION
CYANIDE	A highly poisonous substance that some plants can produce to defend themselves against over-grazing.
CYANOGENESIS	The production of hydrogen cyanide by plants.
CYANOGENIC	The ability of a plant to produce hydrogen cyanide.
CYTOCHROME	An iron-containing protein located on the crista of a mitochondrion. A cytochrome can transfer electrons by reversibly becoming oxidised then reduced.
CYTOCHROME OXIDASE	An enzyme that is the last electron carrier in the cytochrome system. It catalyses the reduction of oxygen to form water.
CYTOPLASM	The viscous fluid found outside the nucleus of a cell.
CYTOSINE	A nitrogenous base found in deoxyribonucleic acid (DNA) and ribonucleic acid (RNA).

D

DAUGHTER CELL	One of two or more cells formed from the division of a single cell.
DAY-NEUTRAL PLANT	A plant whose flowering activity is not linked to the length of day. Dandelions, tomatoes and sunflowers are day-neutral plants.
DEAMINATION	A biochemical process that occurs in the liver by which the amino group is removed from an amino acid and then converted into ammonia.
DEATH RATE	A measure of the percentage of a population that dies within a specified period of time, often a year.
DECARBOXYLASE	An enzyme that catalyses the removal of carbon dioxide from a molecule.
DECAY	The gradual breakdown of something that was once alive.
DECIDUOUS TREE	A tree that sheds its leaves in autumn, with new leaves appearing in the next growing season.
DECOMPOSER	Any living thing that can break down dead material to allow nutrients to be recycled in ecosystems, including bacteria, fungi and worms.
DEFICIENCY DISEASE	Any condition caused by the absence of a particular nutrient such as a vitamin or mineral.

KEYWORD	DEFINITION
DEFORESTATION	The human destruction of forests for use as timber or to release the land for agricultural use without subsequently replanting with new trees. It can cause severe loss of soil as well as changing the environmental conditions for other living things.
DEHYDROGENASE	An enzyme that catalyses the removal of hydrogen from a molecule.
DELETION	A type of mutation in which genetic material is lost from a chromosome. The loss can be as small as a single base or as large as a section from the deoxyribonucleic acid (DNA) molecule.
DEMOGRAPHY	The study of the numbers of people in a particular place and how those numbers change with time.
DENATURATION	An irreversible change in a protein molecule caused by changes in the pH, temperature etc. which renders the activity of the protein useless.
DENDRON	A large fibre that arises from the cell body receiving nerve impulses from other fibres and carrying these towards the cell body.
DENSITY-DEPENDENT FACTOR	Anything whose effect on a population is increased as the size of the population increases. Most factors that are biotic are density-dependent.
DENSITY-INDEPENDENT FACTOR	Anything whose effect on a population is unrelated to the size of that population. Most abiotic factors are density-independent.
DEOXYRIBONUCLEIC ACID	A complex, helically shaped molecule of heredity within which are chemically encoded the instructions to construct, control and reproduce cells by determining the synthesis of protein molecules; abbreviated DNA. It is found in the nucleus and is composed of two sugar-phosphate strands that form the backbone, which is held together by hydrogen bonds across the bases.
DEOXYRIBOSE	A 5-carbon sugar found in deoxyribonucleic acid (DNA).
DESERTIFICATION	Conversion of land that previously might have been used for pasture or crop-growing into desert by overgrazing or overcultivation.
DETERGENT	A cleaning agent that contains a wetting agent, to allow water to penetrate, as well as other ingredients such as enzymes, perfumes and phosphates which can, in excess, have a harmful effect on water supplies and aquatic life.

KEYWORD	DEFINITION
DIABETES	A disorder of metabolism that results in the production of large volumes of urine and a feeling of thirst. It most commonly refers to the condition in which there is a lack of insulin production by the pancreas so that glucose does not easily pass across cell membranes but accumulates in the blood, eventually passing into the urine, taking large volumes of water with it.
DIAPHRAGM	The strong sheet of muscle, separating the thorax from the abdomen, which is important in breathing.
DICOTYLEDON	A plant that possesses two seed-leaves within the seed, as is the case with peas, beans, potatoes etc.
DIET	A general term for the range of nutrients eaten.
DIFFERENTIATION	The process by which cells, usually at an early stage of their development, become committed to grow into various specialised cells.
DIFFUSION	Sometimes referred to as passive transport because it does not require energy, diffusion is the passage of substances down a concentration gradient, from a region of high to low concentration.
DIHYBRID CROSS	A genetic cross involving parents that have two different characteristics which are being investigated. The genes controlling these characteristics are usually on different chromosomes.
DIPLOID	Having two sets of chromosomes.
DIPLOID NUMBER	The total number of homologous chromosomes in a cell nucleus. The human diploid number is 46.
DISACCHARIDE	A sugar such as maltose that is made up of two simpler monosaccharide units such as glucose.
DISCONTINUOUS VARIATION	Variation where the differences in a particular feature fall into distinct categories and cannot be easily measured. Eye colour, blood groups, height in pea plants etc. are examples of discontinuous variation.
DISEASE	Some kind of disorder with marked symptoms and a cause not due to injury of a physical nature.
DIVERGENT EVOLUTION	Another name for adaptive radiation.
DNA POLYMERASE	An enzyme that can catalyse the addition of nucleotides to form a new deoxyribonucleic acid (DNA) strand.

KEYWORD	DEFINITION
DOMINANT ALLELE	The form of a gene that is expressed in the heterozygous condition, masking the effect of the recessive allele.
DORMANCY	The state in which plants are in a state of low metabolism during conditions that are not favourable such as cold, water shortage etc.
DOUBLE HELIX	The characteristic shape of the deoxyribonucleic acid (DNA) molecule, consisting of two strands, each of which turns regularly about itself to form a cylindrical shape, held together by hydrogen bonding.
DOWN'S SYNDROME	A condition caused by the presence of an extra chromosome at position 21 in which the affected individual has slanting eyes, a round-shaped head, flattened nose etc., as well as impaired mental development.
DUODENUM	The upper part of the small intestine into which the contents of the stomach empty. It connects to the liver and pancreas via the bile and pancreatic ducts, respectively.
DUPLICATION	A type of mutation in which part of a chromosome is copied next to an identical part so producing extra copies of the sequence of genes in that duplicated section and making the chromosome longer.

E

ECDYSIS	The shedding or moulting process in insects by which the old outer covering is split and cast to be replaced by a new, soft covering which eventually hardens.
ECHOLOCATION	The technique used by some animals such as dolphins and bats for finding objects that cannot be seen in the normal way. It involves the sending out of high-frequency sounds and detecting their return.
ECOLOGICAL BALANCE	The harmonious, stable interplay of all the elements that go to make up a particular part of the environment, including the plants and animals which live there.
ECOLOGICAL BARRIER	The means by which a species becomes divided into two or more sub-groups based on some change in the environment such as differing temperature. This then prevents the groups from continuing to interbreed.

KEYWORD	DEFINITION
ECOSYSTEM	A complex community of different species of animals and plants that are dependent on each other and their environment.
ECTOTHERM	An organism that is unable to maintain a constant internal temperature and is therefore dependent to a large extent on the environment to regulate this.
EDAPHIC FACTOR	Any factor in the environment that is related to the soil such as its pH and texture.
EFFECTOR	A specialized group of cells that bring about activity in a muscle or a gland as a result of stimulation either by a nerve impulse or the action of a hormone.
EFFLUENT	Any liquid, such as treated or untreated sewage, discharged from a source into the environment.
ELASTIN	A fibrous protein forming the major structural part of elastic tissues such as the skin.
ELECTRON MICROSCOPE	A microscope that uses a beam of electrons instead of visible light to "illuminate" an object for viewing. It is capable of very high magnification and resolution.
ELECTRON TRANSFER SYSTEM	A series of biochemical steps that occur on mitochondrial cristae during aerobic respiration. Each step requires its own specific carrier molecule, which picks up and transfers hydrogen atoms from the Krebs cycle until the hydrogen atoms ultimately combine with oxygen to form water.
EMIGRATION	The movement of animals away from a particular place.
EMULSION	A liquid in which droplets of one substance, such as fat, are suspended in another, such as water, without actually dissolving.
ENDANGERED SPECIES	Any species that is on the brink of extinction, often due to the activities of humans.
ENDEMIC	Restricted to a particular area or group of organisms.
ENDOCYTOSIS	The energy-demanding process by which cells can surround a small particle and form a vesicle. It includes both phagocytosis and pinocytosis.
ENDOGENOUS	Having its origin within the body of the organism being studied.
ENDONUCLEASE	An enzyme that can split a nucleic acid at a particular position.

KEYWORD	DEFINITION
ENDOPLASMIC RETICULUM	A network of membranes that can store and transport proteins and fats for use elsewhere in the cell.
ENDOSPERM	A food source found in many plant seeds that is used by the embryo plant, for example, in barley.
ENDOTHERM	An organism that can maintain a constant internal temperature independent of the environmental temperature.
ENVELOPE	A layer of lipid and protein found on the capsid of certain viruses.
ENVIRONMENTAL FACTOR	A variable that is not genetically based and can affect a person's development. For example diet, parental influence, social and cultural aspects.
ENVIRONMENTAL SINK	Part of the environment that receives and stores materials produced either naturally or otherwise. For example, plants can act as a sink for carbon dioxide gas or a body of water can absorb heat produced by a factory.
ENZYME	A specific organic catalyst produced in cells which can speed up biochemical reactions without being altered. It is made of large, complex protein molecules.
ENZYME INDUCTION	The production of an enzyme which is activated by the presence of its substrate.
EPIDERMIS	In a multicellular animal or plant, the outer layer of cells. Often this is only one cell thick in plants and invertebrates.
EPITHELIUM	A collection of similarly shaped and sized cells that cover external body surfaces as well as lining body cavities.
EROSION	The wearing away, slowly or rapidly, of rock or soil, which can be due to weathering or the effects of human activity such as deforestation.
ERYTHROCYTE	Another name for a red blood cell that has no nucleus and contains haemoglobin, and whose function is oxygen transportation.
ETHANOL	Ethyl alcohol, produced by yeasts fermenting sugars.
ETIOLATION	The unusually long appearance of plant stems grown in the absence of light. The stems are also very yellow due to the lack of pigment production.

KEYWORD	DEFINITION
EUTROPHICATION	A general term for the various effects of an increase in nutrients in a body of water. This causes algae to flourish excessively then decay, and this is followed by a massive increase in decomposing bacteria, which deplete the water of oxygen and cause the death of those living things that need oxygenated water.
EVAPORATION	The change in state of a liquid into a gas below that liquid's boiling point.
EVOLUTION	The process by which living things have gradually changed over a very long period of time to become better suited to survive and reproduce in their environment.
EXCRETION	The elimination of wastes, such as urine and carbon dioxide, which have been produced by an organism.
EXOCYTOSIS	The process by which a membrane-bound vesicle fuses with the cell's plasma membrane so that the contents of the vesicle are discharged to the outside of the cell.
EXOSKELETON	The skeleton found on the outside of an animal such as an insect or crab.
EXPONENTIAL GROWTH PHASE	A pattern of growth that is unchecked by limitation of factors which might otherwise inhibit or restrict that growth.
EXTINCTION	The total loss of an organism from the planet.
EXTRACELLULAR ENZYME	An enzyme that acts outside the cell which made it; for example, digestive enzymes are generally extracellular.

F

KEYWORD	DEFINITION
FACTOR VIII	A globular protein that is necessary for the proper clotting of blood. The absence of this factor causes haemophilia.
FAECES	The semi-solid waste expelled from the gut.
FALLOW	Land that has been left for a season unploughed or unsown after having been previously used to grow crops etc.
FAMINE	The severe, prolonged scarcity of food.
FAT	A class of chemicals that includes lipids (solid at room temperature) and oils (liquid at room temperature). The main fats consist of three molecules of fatty acids and one of glycerol. Fats are important stores of energy, as well as insulators, and provide mechanical cushioning.

KEYWORD	DEFINITION
FATTY ACID	A class of chemicals that, when combined with glycerol, form fats. Fatty acids may be saturated, where there are no double bonds formed between carbon atoms, or unsaturated, where there is at least one such double bond.
FAUNA	The collective term for the animals in a particular environment.
FERTILE OFFSPRING	Young that can interbreed to form more of the same kind.
FERTILIZER	Any agent, produced either naturally or artificially, added to soil to enhance its properties in some way.
FIBROUS PROTEIN	Protein that is generally insoluble, such as collagen, formed by several parallel strands of polypeptides, held together to confer strength and elasticity.
FIGHT-OR-FLIGHT REACTION	The collective name for the set of reactions to a situation that is stressful in some way. It results in raised blood pressure and increased heart and breathing rates, mediated mainly by the hormone adrenaline.
FIRST FILIAL GENERATION	In genetics, the offspring produced as a result of a parental cross.
FLACCID	As applied to plants and their cells, a state of being wilted due to excessive water loss.
FLORA	The general term for the plant life in a particular environment.
FLUID-MOSAIC MEMBRANE MODEL	The current model to represent the structure of a cell membrane as composed of two layers of phospholipid with floating protein molecules. The membrane is not a fixed structure, because the phospholipids can move, as can the protein molecules.
FOETAL ALCOHOL SYNDROME	A collection of symptoms manifest in a newborn baby whose mother has been drinking alcohol excessively during the pregnancy. These include low birth mass, poor growth of the upper jaw, an unusually long upper lip, mental retardation and hollowed breastbone.
FOETUS	A young mammal in its early stages of development and still within the mother's uterus. In humans this would be about 7–8 weeks and older.
FOOD CHAIN	A simple, linear representation of the feeding relationship of animals and plants.

KEYWORD	DEFINITION
FOOD VACUOLE	A membrane-bound sac within a cell where small particles of food are held.
FOOD WEB	A complex set of feeding relationships between animals and plants, consisting of many linked food chains.
FOOT AND MOUTH DISEASE	A highly contagious, viral infection affecting practically all cloven-footed mammals, including cattle, sheep, goats and pigs; also found in wild herbivores such as bison, deer, antelope, reindeer, llamas and camels.
FORAGING	Animal behaviour associated with collection of food.
FOSSIL	The preserved remains of plants or animals.
FOSSIL FUEL	A finite energy source formed from the remains of dead animals and plants such as coal, oil and gas.
FRAMESHIFT MUTATION	A mutation in which one or two bases are inserted into or deleted from a gene so that every codon after the mutation is affected and therefore every amino acid coded for is different, producing a mutant protein.
FRUCTOSE	A reducing monosaccharide occurring in fruits, honey etc; this is the sweetest of the sugars.
FRUIT FLY	*Drosophila*. A small insect favoured by geneticists.
FUNGICIDE	Any agent that is capable of killing a fungus.
FUNGUS	An organism that is heterotrophic and has no chlorophyll. Fungal cell walls are made of chitin. Fungi reproduce mainly by spores.

G

GALACTOSE	A reducing monosaccharide occurring as a natural product of the digestion of milk sugar, lactose.
GALL BLADDER	A small, pear-shaped sac that stores bile and lies underneath the liver.
GAMETE	A sex cell, either sperm or ovum, that possesses only half the diploid number of chromosomes.
GENE	The basic unit of heredity, corresponding to a length of deoxyribonucleic acid (DNA), occupying a particular place on the chromosome and that may exist in alternate forms called alleles.

KEYWORD	DEFINITION
GENE FREQUENCY	How often a particular allele occurs in a population.
GENE LOCUS	The particular place on a chromosome where a gene is located.
GENE MIGRATION	The introduction of new alleles into a population when organisms enter from a different population whose gene pool is not the same.
GENE MUTATION	A change to one or more of the bases in the deoxyribonucleic acid (DNA) molecule, sometimes called a point mutation.
GENE POOL	All the alleles in a population of interbreeding individuals.
GENE PROBE	A single strand of deoxyribonucleic acid (DNA) used to locate a particular gene whose base sequence is complementary. The probe is usually labelled with radioactive phosphorus.
GENETIC CODE	A linear sequence of triplets of bases on the deoxyribonucleic acid (DNA) molecule that codes for a particular protein.
GENETIC DRIFT	Random changes in the occurrence of a particular gene.
GENETIC ENGINEERING	A generalised term for the techniques used to deliberately alter the deoxyribonucleic acid (DNA) of a cell by, for example, inserting part or all of a gene. The altered DNA is then described as recombinant and can be used to produce human insulin, hormones etc. It is increasingly possible to repair faulty DNA in genetic defects, in some cases by recombinant technology.
GENETIC EQUILIBRIUM	The situation when the frequency of particular genes in a population remains relatively stable over a period of time.
GENOME	All the genetic material in a particular organism.
GENOTYPE	The collective term for all the alleles possessed by an animal or plant.
GEOGRAPHICAL BARRIER	The means by which a species becomes divided into two or more sub-groups based on some major physical obstacle that prevents the groups from continuing to interbreed. For example, small birds being blown onto different islands and not able to return to their original environment.

KEYWORD	DEFINITION
GIBBERELLIN	A plant growth substance that exists in many forms. It causes stem elongation, breaks seed dormancy and induces enzyme production in these seeds to utilise stored food etc.
GIGANTISM	Excessive body growth, manifested in extreme tallness, usually associated with over-production of the pituitary growth hormone in early development.
GLOBAL WARMING	The slow increase in the Earth's surface-air temperature caused by the accumulation of carbon dioxide gas in the atmosphere. This has the effect of trapping solar radiation that would otherwise be reflected back into space. It is sometimes called the "greenhouse effect".
GLOBULAR PROTEIN	A compact, rounded protein that is folded and twisted into a tertiary structure and usually insoluble in water. Enzymes are a major group of globular proteins.
GLOMERULUS	A tight knot of tiny blood vessels found in the kidney of vertebrate animals that allows small molecules such as water, glucose and urea to filter out under pressure.
GLUCAGON	A hormone produced by the pancreas which causes the glycogen in the liver to break down into glucose.
GLUCOSE	A simple, 6-carbon monosaccharide that is a major substrate for respiration; glucose is soluble in water.
GLYCERATE-3-PHOSPHATE	A 3-carbon molecule formed during the light-independent stage of photosynthesis. It is made when ribulose biphosphate combines with carbon dioxide.
GLYCEROL	An alcohol that is a basic component of fat molecules.
GLYCOGEN	The main polysaccharide stored in the liver which is made up of many glucose molecules in a branched arrangement. Glycogen is insoluble and is osmotically inactive.
GLYCOLYSIS	The initial series of reactions in respiration that takes place in the cytoplasm and does not require oxygen. Two molecules each of pyruvic acid and adenosine triphosphate (ATP) are formed from one molecule of glucose.
GLYCOPROTEIN	A conjugated protein that has sugar as part of its structure. Some enzymes, antigens etc. are glycoproteins.
GOBLET CELL	A mucus-secreting cell found in the lining of the respiratory and intestinal tracts, so called because of its shape, which is like a wine glass.

KEYWORD	DEFINITION
GOLGI BODY	A membranous structure found in the cell derived from vesicles pinched off the endoplasmic reticulum. It may have a storage function, as well as facilitating the assembly of complex molecules such as glycoproteins from simpler ones such as carbohydrates and proteins.
GRAIN	With reference to trees, the patterning due to the annual rings being cut at particular angles.
GRANUM	The disc-like folded membrane found in the chloroplast and that holds the photosynthetic molecules such as chlorophyll.
GRATICULE	A glass slide carrying a very precisely constructed grid used for measurement of cell sizes etc.
GREEN REVOLUTION	An umbrella term for all the different strategies used to improve the yield of crops using artificially selected varieties, fertilizers etc. from the 1960s onwards.
GREENHOUSE EFFECT	The slow increase in the earth's surface-air temperature caused by the accumulation of carbon dioxide gas in the atmosphere. This has the effect of trapping solar radiation that would otherwise be reflected back into space. Sometimes called "global warming".
GROWTH	The irreversible increase in the size of an organism associated with cell division followed by cell enlargement.
GROWTH CURVE	A graphical representation of the change in height or other variable factor associated with growth with respect to time.
GROWTH HORMONE	A hormone produced by the pituitary gland which stimulates the growth of the skeleton and protein synthesis; sometimes called "somatotrophic hormone".
GROWTH SPURT	A stage of rapid growth either during the first 2 years of life or at puberty.
GUANINE	A nitrogenous base found in deoxyribonucleic acid (DNA) and ribonucleic acid (RNA).
GUARD CELL	A specialised cell that surrounds a stoma. Changes in its water content can cause it to bend or straighten.
GULLET	An alternative name for the oesophagus.

KEYWORD	DEFINITION
H	
HABITAT	A general term for the place in an environment where a plant or animal lives.
HABITUATION	In behaviour this refers to a decrease in the response of an animal to repeated exposure to the same stimulus.
HAEMOGLOBIN	A conjugated globular protein that transports oxygen by reversibly combining with it to form oxyhaemoglobin in the lungs and then off-loading the oxygen in respiring tissues.
HAEMOGLOBIN S	An abnormal form of haemoglobin produced in individuals with the genetic condition sickle-cell anaemia. Haemoglobin S precipitates when the oxygen tension is low, causing the red blood cells to adopt a sickle shape and rupture.
HAEMOLYSIS	The destruction of red blood cells as a result of them being in an environment with a high water content, being old, being attacked by antibodies etc.
HAEMOPHILIA	A sex-linked recessive condition in which the blood clots very poorly, often due to lack of a blood protein called factor VIII.
HAPLOID NUMBER	The number of chromosomes present in a sex cell such as a sperm or ovum. In humans the haploid number is 23.
HEART	The powerful, muscular double pump situated in the thorax behind the breastbone.
HEAVY METAL	A metal with a high density which can be used in the preparation of specimens to be examined in the electron microscope. A heavy metal shadows the specimen to enhance the contrast between different parts.
HELPER T-CELL	A type of lymphocyte that has an important role to play in the proper functioning of the immune response.
HEPATITIS	The general term for various types of viral infections of the liver.
HERBICIDE	A chemical used to kill plants whose growth in a particular place is undesirable.
HERBIVORE	An animal that feeds only on plants, sometimes called a primary consumer.

KEYWORD	DEFINITION
HETEROGAMETIC	With reference to the formation of sperm, describing the mother cell that has two different sex chromosomes, X and Y.
HETEROTROPHIC NUTRITION	A type of feeding based on taking in organic substances in the form of plants and/or animals.
HETEROZYGOTE	An individual who carries different alleles of the same gene(s).
HIBERNATION	A state of low metabolism and body temperature entered into by animals during winter. It allows the animal to survive when resources are scarce. Usually true hibernation is found in small animals such as hamsters, hedgehogs etc.
HIERARCHY	In behaviour, usually a social system within which individuals will compete against each other for position within the group.
HOMEOSTASIS	The general term for the maintenance of body systems in a state of dynamic equilibrium through a series of feedback mechanisms.
HOMOGAMETIC	With reference to the formation of eggs, describing the mother cell that has sex chromsomes which are the same, all X.
HOMOLOGOUS CHROMOSOMES	Chromosomes that are the same size and shape, possessing the same pattern of genes along their lengths, but the genes may have different allelic forms.
HOMOLOGY	Seen when structures that have different functions share a common plan, suggesting they share the same ancestry; for example, the wing of a bat and the arm of a human.
HOMOZYGOTE	An individual who carries identical alleles of the same gene(s).
HORMONE	A chemical produced by one part of an animal or plant body transported to target receptive organs and/or tissues to affect their function and/or structure.
HOST	An organism which provides a favourable environment for the growth of another.
HUMAN IMMUNODEFICIENCY VIRUS	The viral cause of acquired immune deficiency syndrome.
HUMIDITY	A measure of the water content of the atmosphere.

KEYWORD	DEFINITION
HUMUS	The end-product of the breakdown of dead animal and plant materials near the surface of the soil.
HUNTER-GATHERER EXISTENCE	A lifestyle based on hunting animals and gathering plant food; there is no cultivation of crops or other agricultural practices.
HYBRID	An animal or plant that is a cross-breed, the result of crossing two pure parental strains for a particular inheritable feature.
HYBRIDISATION	The formation of a hybrid animal or plant often used by humans to produce a particular plant or animal with desirable features.
HYBRID VIGOUR	The increased quality, normally of a plant, as a result of reproduction by two parents from different strains of one species or occasionally from two different species; for example, an increase in mass, height or growth rate might result.
HYDROGEN ACCEPTOR	A chemical which can form a reversible bond with hydrogen.
HYDROGEN BOND	A weak force that is responsible for much of the secondary and tertiary structures of molecules such as proteins and nucleic acids.
HYDROGEN PEROXIDE	A powerful oxidizing agent formed in various metabolic processes and capable of causing rapid cell damage. It is broken down instantaneously by the enzyme catalase.
HYDROPHILIC	Having a positive affinity for the water molecule, for example as does the phosphate head of a phospholipid molecule.
HYDROPHOBIC	Having a negative affinity for the water molecule, for example as does the fatty acid tail of a phospholipid molecule.
HYDROPHYTE	A plant that prefers wet environments in which to grow.
HYPERTONIC	Of a solution that in relation to another has a greater solute concentration.
HYPOTHALAMUS	The region of brain associated with regulating body temperature, sleep patterns, feeding, drinking etc. It is also the site of attachment of the pituitary gland.
HYPOTHESIS	The best scientific "guess" to explain observations that can be subjected to rigorous investigation to test its validity.

KEYWORD	DEFINITION
HYPOTONIC	Of a solution that in relation to another has a lower solute concentration.

I

KEYWORD	DEFINITION
IMMIGRATION	The movement of animals into a particular area.
IMMOBILISATION	The technique of attaching an enzyme to a support system, such as a gel, so that it can be used over and over again. A continuous flow of substrate is passed over the gel, often in the form of beads, to allow the enzymatic conversion to take place.
IMMUNE SYSTEM	The collective name for the cells, tissues and organs within the body which bring about a response to an antigen and may allow the development of long-term immunity.
IMMUNISATION	The method of giving a person protection, either temporary or permanent, either natural or artificial, against an infectious agent. Sometimes called "vaccination".
IMMUNITY	The state of being able to resist infection or the effects of a toxin etc.
IMMUNOGLOBIN	The general term for a protein antibody.
IMMUNOSUPPRESSIVE DRUG	A drug administered to patients who have had transplants of organs or tissues to subdue the normal immune response that would otherwise cause rejection. Since these drugs suppress the immune system, the patients are therefore more liable to succumb to infections.
IMPLANTATION	Penetration by the fertilized egg into the wall of the uterus.
IMPRINTING	In behaviour this refers to the inborn, rapid fixation-type response of a new-born animal towards its mother or siblings.
INBORN ERROR OF METABOLISM	A biochemical abnormality such as phenylketonuria that is genetically based. It often is the result of a missing or faulty enzyme, which causes a breakdown in a particular metabolic pathway so that intermediates build up to toxic levels.
INBREEDING	The sexual reproduction between closely related plants or animals which can lead to a deterioration of continued viability because of the accumulation of mutations.

KEYWORD	DEFINITION
INBREEDING DEPRESSION	The effect of continued inbreeding which results in an increase in the proportion of offspring that have numbers of mutations.
INCOMPLETE DOMINANCE	Where neither allele of a pair controlling a particular characteristic is completely dominant over the other and both alleles are partially expressed, for example sickle-cell anaemia.
INDEPENDENT ASSORTMENT	The mixing up of genetic material during meiosis which results from the random distribution of maternal and paternal chromosomes into the gametes. The two alleles of a gene segregate into different gametes independently of the alleles of another gene. Independent assortment is a major factor in the cause of genetic variation between individuals.
INDICATOR SPECIES	An organism whose presence or absence is an index of the condition of the habitat. For example, the presence of bloodworms in water indicates that it is likely to be polluted and have low levels of oxygen.
INDOLE ACETIC ACID	One of the best-studied auxins.
INDUCTION	With respect to enzyme production, the manufacture of an enzyme by a specific set of genes being transcribed in response to a stimulus such as the presence of the substrate.
INDUSTRIAL MELANISM	The dominance of a particular animal type by the dark form compared with the normal, light-coloured variety in areas that are particularly industrialised; seen, for example, in the melanic form of the peppered moth on sooty trees.
INHERITED FACTOR	Anything genetically inherited that can influence development.
INSECT GALL	An abnormal growth on a leaf or stem caused by the young of some insects.
INSECTICIDE	A chemical that will kill an insect usually deemed to be a pest or a potential health hazard.
INSERTION	A mutation consisting of the addition of one of more bases into a DNA sequence which causes a frameshift reading error in translation.
INSULATION	A general term for anything that protects in some way, which may be used, for example, to describe the ability of fat to prevent loss of heat, to form a mechanical cushion round organs, or to prevent nerve impulses travelling sideways from one fibre to another.

KEYWORD	DEFINITION
INSULIN	A hormone produced in the pancreas that regulates the blood glucose level by stimulating the uptake of glucose across cell membranes and the conversion of glucose into glycogen for storage in the liver and muscles.
INTERCELLULAR	Among or between cells or found in the spaces between cells.
INTERFERON	A glycoprotein molecule produced by cells of mammals which have been infected with a virus. Although it does not have any effect on the virus itself, it does confer some protection on other cells to help prevent them becoming infected.
INTERNAL ENVIRONMENT	A general term for all the body cells and the fluids associated with them which are kept in a steady state by homeostatic mechanisms.
INTERNODE	Between the points of attachment of the leaves on a stem.
INTERPHASE	The time after cell division has taken place when the nucleus is not dividing, nor are any changes visible, but nucleic acids may be copied and proteins synthesised.
INTERSPECIFIC COMPETITION	The competition between organisms of different species for the same resources, for example light, nutrients and space.
INTRACELLULAR	Within a cell.
INTRACELLULAR ENZYME	An enzyme, such as a dehydrogenase, which works inside a cell.
INTRASPECIFIC COMPETITION	The competition between organisms of the same species for the same resources, for example light, nutrients and space.
INVERSION	A form of mutation in which a chromosomal sequence is removed and replaced the opposite way round.
INVOLUNTARY MUSCLE	Another name for smooth muscle.
IODINE SOLUTION	A reagent used to test for the presence of starch by changing colour from red-brown to very dark blue/black.
ISOLATION	The separation of two potentially breeding groups of the same original population.
ISOTONIC	Describing two solutions that have the same concentration of solutes.

KEYWORD	DEFINITION

J

| JACOB-MONOD HYPOTHESIS | The suggested mechanism by which the regulation of gene activity might take place; sometimes called the operon model. |

K

KARYOTYPE	Chromosomes found in a somatic cell nucleus classified according to their size and shape. A normal human male/female karyotype would be 46, XY/XX
KERATIN	A fibrous, insoluble protein that is the main constituent of nail, hair, skin etc.
KIDNEY	One of a pair of bean-shaped organs lying towards the back of the abdomen. The kidneys are responsible for regulating the water balance of the blood as well as removing potentially harmful substances from the plasma by producing a sterile solution known as urine.
KIDNEY TUBULE	A small, narrow tube forming part of the filter unit of the kidney.
KLEINFELTER'S SYNDROME	A genetic condition in males caused by an extra X chromosome which has a feminising effect on the phenotype of the male; for example, there may be breast development, with absence of facial and body hair.
KREBS CYCLE	A cyclical series of biochemical reactions that occur in the matrix of a mitochondrion in the presence of oxygen. Carbon dioxide is released and hydrogen atoms are fed into the electron transport chain on the cristae of the mitochondrion, which allows for the synthesis of adenosine triphosphate molecules.

L

| LACTIC ACID | A compound formed as an end-product of anaerobic glucose metabolism during strenuous exercise. The pyruvic acid formed from glycolysis is reduced to lactic acid, which can cause muscle cramp. |

KEYWORD	DEFINITION
LACTOSE	A dissacharide consisting of a glucose and galactose molecule joined together, commonly found in milk.
LAMELLA	A layer of folded membrane found between the grana of the chloroplast.
LAND BRIDGE	The physical connections that still exist between continents.
LATERAL MERISTEM	The growth area in the stem of a plant whose activity causes an increase in the width of the stem. Cambium is an example of a lateral meristem.
LEACHING	The process by which dissolved substances, such as phosphates and nitrates in the soil, are washed out by rainwater, possibly ending up in nearby streams or rivers.
LEAF CANOPY	The collective name for the leaves and branches which form the top layer in a woodland. This layer can have marked effect on the quality of light reaching lower plants as well as restricting the volume of water they receive.
LEAF MOSAIC DISEASE	A viral disease of plants that shows itself as strands of yellow colouring on the leaves to form a random pattern.
LEAF PRIMORDIUM	An early stage in the production of a leaf.
LEARNING	The process by which an animal's behaviour will become modified on the basis of experience.
LEUCOPLAST	The colourless structure found in plant cells which stores starch and oils.
LICHEN	A symbiotic association between an alga and a fungus, the latter making up almost 90% of the mass of the combination. Lichens are very common on the bark of trees and their presence or absence is often used as an indicator of the absence or presence, respectively, of air pollution.
LIFE EXPECTANCY	A statistical prediction of the likely number of years a person will live.
LIGAMENT	A bundle of strong, fibrous animal protein, mainly collagen, which acts as a binding and supporting material, especially in and around joints. Ligaments are very strong and flexible, but inelastic.
LIGASE	An enzyme that is capable of joining two detached strands of nucleic acid.

KEYWORD	DEFINITION
LIGHT-DEPENDENT STAGE OF PHOTOSYNTHESIS	The stage at which light energy is trapped and used to make adenosine triphosphate and reduced nicotinamide dinucleotide phosophate to be used in the light-independent stage. It involves the splitting of water molecules by photolysis and occurs in the grana of the chloroplast.
LIGHT-INDEPENDENT STAGE OF PHOTOSYNTHESIS	The stage at which carbon dioxide is reduced to form glucose using adenosine triphosphate and reduced nicotinamide dinucleotide phosphate generated in the light-dependent stage. Sometimes called the Calvin cycle, it occurs in the stroma of the chloroplast.
LIGNIN	A biopolymer found in some plant cell walls which it stiffens and helps stop infection and decay. It makes the cell woody.
LIMITING FACTOR	In ecology, a variable, such as disease or predation, whose presence will limit the numbers in a population. In biochemistry, a variable, such as the concentration of an enzyme, whose absence will slow down or inhibit a reaction so that the amount of product is reduced.
LINKED GENES	Genes that are located on the same chromosome.
LIPASE	A general term for an enzyme that can break down fat into fatty acids and glycerol.
LIPID	A chemical consisting of glycerol and fatty acids which are important as cell membrane components, coverings for nerves, insulators etc. Lipids are insoluble in water but soluble in ethanol.
LIPOPROTEIN	A water-soluble protein found in the plasma which is combined with fat. Lipoproteins are important for transporting fats in blood and lymph.
LOCK-AND-KEY MECHANISM	A model to represent the specificity of the enzyme–substrate complex.
LOCUS	The actual position of a particular gene on a chromosome.
LONG BONE	Bones such as the femur in the leg whose lengths are considerably greater than their width.
LONG-DAY PLANT	A plant that requires a length of day in excess of some critical value before it will flower. Spinach, lettuce and grass are examples of long-day plants.
LOOP OF HENLÉ	The U-shaped part of the kidney tubule along which water containing dissolved substances travels.

KEYWORD	DEFINITION
LYMPHOCYTE	A type of white blood cell present also in lymph nodes, spleen, thymus, bone marrow and the wall of the gut. Lymphocytes are primarily involved in body defence.
LYSIS	Break-up of a cell.
LYSOSOME	A single membrane-bound organelle found in cytoplasm which contains powerful digestive enzymes and may be produced by Golgi apparatus. It is involved in breakdown of ingested food particles and can also cause the complete destruction of the cell after its useful life is over, in a process known as autolysis.

M

KEYWORD	DEFINITION
MACROELEMENT	A chemical required in relatively large amounts for the proper growth and development of a plant. Such chemicals include nitrogen, phosphorus, potassium and magnesium.
MACRONUCLEUS	The larger of two nuclei found in the ciliated, one-celled organisms such as *Paramecium*. Its function is the same as the nucleus found in the cells of higher animals.
MALARIA	An infectious disease caused by a one-celled organism called *Plasmodium*. It is spread by the bite of mosquitoes.
MALTOSE	A dissacharide, consisting of two glucose molecules joined together, which is produced by enzymatic digestion of starch or glycogen. Maltose is found in germinating seeds.
MAMMARY GLAND	A gland found in the female breast which secretes milk.
MANOMETER	Apparatus that is used to measure pressure in a gas or liquid. In its simplest form, it consists of a U-shaped tube containing water or some other liquid, with one end connected to the structure whose pressure is being measured while the other end is open to the atmosphere.
MARGINAL LAND	Land bordering an area used for cultivating crops which is usually not suitable for growing.
MARSUPIAL MAMMAL	An animal that does not have a placenta. The young animal is housed in a pouch after birth.
MAXIMUM SUSTAINABLE YIELD	The upper limit of a crop of plants or animals which can be harvested without long-term harmful effects on the population.

KEYWORD	DEFINITION
MEDULLA	The general term for the inner area of an organ or tissue, as distinct from its outer area, which is often referred to as the cortex.
MEIOSIS	A type of cell division associated with sexual reproduction which reduces the chromosomal content by half of the original number. Meiosis is an important mechanism for ensuring constancy of the chromosome number as well as generating genetic variation. Sperm and eggs are produced through meiotic division.
MELANIN	A natural, dark brown-coloured pigment in skin, hair, iris of the eye etc. Production of melanin is stimulated by sunlight to protect underlying tissues from radiation damage.
MEMORY CELL	A special type of white blood cell that remains in the blood after recovery from an infection and which can mount a rapid response to the same antigen encountered later.
MENDEL'S FIRST LAW	Cells contain two alleles for each gene, and these alleles will separate independently of each other into different gametes during meiosis.
MENDEL'S SECOND LAW	Providing two inheritable features are controlled by genes that are located on two different chromosomes, they will combine randomly in meiosis.
MERISTEM	The area of a plant that is actively dividing, found at root and shoot tips, as well in stems.
MESOPHYLL	The internal layers of cells in a plant leaf that lie between the upper and lower epidermis. Mesophyll is usually photosynthetic.
MESOPHYTE	A plant that grows in an environment which is neither too wet nor too dry.
MESSENGER RIBONUCLEIC ACID	A nucleic acid that carries information from the deoxyribonucleic acid (DNA) in the nucleus into the cytoplasm to the ribosomes for translation into a protein; abbreviated mRNA.
METABOLIC PATHWAY	A biochemical sequence of enzyme-controlled reactions changing one substance into another which eventually leads to the formation of a product. Such a sequence may be linear or cyclical.
METABOLIC RATE	A measure of the rate of body metabolism that is very temperature-sensitive.

KEYWORD	DEFINITION
METABOLISM	The collective term for all biochemical reactions occurring in a cell.
METABOLITE	A chemical which is part of any biochemical process.
METHANE	Sometimes called "marsh gas" on account of its presence in stagnant pools, methane gas also arises naturally from the anaerobic breakdown of sewage and can be used as a fuel.
MICRO-IRRIGATION	A relatively recently developed technique of supplying water to crops using a series of pipes which have small holes in them set close to the plant roots so that less water is used than by conventional methods.
MICRONUCLEUS	The smaller of the two nuclei found in the ciliated, one-celled organisms such as *Paramecium*; it has an important role in the reproductive process.
MIGRATION	The movement, usually over long distances, of animals linked to seasonal changes.
MIMICRY	When one animal resembles another unrelated animal in some protective way such as warning colour or smell so that a possible predator will confuse the two and avoid eating the harmless animal.
MINERAL	In the diet, a chemical required, usually in very small amounts, for proper health; it includes calcium, iron, magnesium etc.
MITOCHONDRION	A double membrane-bound, cylindrically shaped organelle found in varying numbers in cytoplasm of cells which is the site of aerobic respiration, producing adenosine triphosphate (ATP) for cell function.
MITOSIS	A type of nuclear division that results in the formation of two new daughter cells, each of which has the same genetic complement as the other and the original parent cell from which they arose.
MOBILE	Being able to move from one place to another.
MONOCOTYLEDON	A flowering plant that has only seed leaf in the embryo plant. These plants include daffodils, tulips, grasses and maize.
MONOCULTURE	An agricultural process in which one crop, such as barley, is grown to the exclusion of all others.
MONOHYBRID INHERITANCE	An inheritance pattern involving one gene controlling a single character.

KEYWORD	DEFINITION
MONOSACCHARIDE	A simple sugar that can be broken down into a smaller monomer that has the general formula $(CH_2O)_n$.
MORATORIUM	A voluntary ban on the exploitation of some animal or plant in order to minimise the risk of causing its possible extinction.
MOSAIC PATTERNING	The arrangement of leaves in a plant such that one leaf does not lie directly above another, thereby avoiding shading this leaf.
MOTIVATION	The drive which shapes the behaviour of an animal to achieve a particular aim.
MUCUS	The sticky, viscous material secreted by mucous membranes, which line the body cavities that lead to the outside, such as the digestive and urinary tracts, which acts as a barrier or lubricant.
MULTICELLULAR	Describing an organism whose body is made up of many cells.
MUSCULAR DYSTROPHY	An inherited condition that results in wasting of the muscles.
MUTAGEN	A general term for any agent that can induce a change in the DNA without necessarily resulting in the death of the cells concerned. Ionizing radiation such as ultraviolet light, X-rays and gamma rays, and chemical agents such as tars in cigarette smoke and mustard gas are mutagens. Some viruses can act as mutagens.
MUTAGENIC AGENT	A factor that can cause change in genetic material, for example radiation and certain chemicals.
MUTANT	An individual in which there has been some change to the deoxyribonucleic acid (DNA). The effect may or may not be visible.
MUTATION	Any change in the genetic make-up of a cell that can result in an altered phenotype effectively producing a new allele if only a gene is affected or a change in the number of chromosomes. If the change is in sex cells then mutation may be passed to offspring.
MYOSIN	A protein found in thick filaments of skeletal muscle myofibrils.

KEYWORD	DEFINITION
N	
NATURAL CYCLE	A process occurring in nature by which the conditions at the end are the same as at the start. For example, the carbon cycle takes in carbon dioxide from the air in photosynthesis but then releases it again in respiration or decomposition.
NATURAL IMMUNITY	Immunity associated with possessing a particular genotype rather than that produced by artificial exposure to an antigen through vaccination. It does not require previous encounter of the invading antigen.
NEGATIVE FEEDBACK CONTROL	The most common type of corrective mechanism found in the body for restoring and maintaining its dynamic state of equilibrium in which a departure from a set value for some variable is detected by a receptor and a response made which corrects that departure so that the signal is then stopped.
NERVE FIBRE	Any of the long, thin processes that emerge from the cell body of a neurone which can transmit nerve impulses.
NICHE	The role played by a particular organism in the environment which is usually a function of the food eaten and a range of variables tolerated such as temperature, light intensity etc.
NICOTINAMIDE ADENINE DINUCLEOTIDE	A coenzyme that accepts hydrogen atoms required in small amounts in redox-type reactions; associated with the Krebs cycle and electron transport chain. Abbreviated NAD.
NICOTINAMIDE ADENINE DINUCLEOTIDE PHOSPHATE	Phosphorylated form of NAD. Abbreviated to NADP.
NICOTINE	A potent chemical derived from the tobacco plant which is highly toxic to most animals, interfering with the proper working of the junction between nerves and muscles. Nicotine is found in cigarette smoke.
NON-DISJUNCTION	A condition in which pairs of homologous chromosomes or the two sister chromatids of a chromosome fail to separate properly in meiotic cell division, resulting in daughter cells that have an abnormal number of chromosomes. Non-disjunction can affect both autosomes and sex chromosomes.
NON-REDUCING SUGAR	A dissacharide sugar that fails to give a positive result with Benedict's or Fehling's reagents.
NON-SELECTIVE WEEDKILLER	A chemical that will kill all plants indiscriminately.

KEYWORD	DEFINITION
NON-SPECIFIC IMMUNITY	A generalised term for defence against an antigen which does not require previous exposure. Non-specific immunity includes stomach acid, tears, coughing etc.
NORMAL DISTRIBUTION	A typical distribution associated with a continuous variation such as height or weight, usually resulting in a bell-shaped graph when frequency is plotted against the variable.
NUCLEAR PORE	A site on the nuclear membrane where the double membranes are joined to form a small opening that allows connection between the nuclear contents and the cytoplasm. Ribosomes and messenger ribonucleic acid (mRNA) can leave through these openings, while adenosine triphosphate (ATP) and monomers such as nucleotides can enter.
NUCLEOLUS	An organelle found within the nucleus, occupying nearly a quarter of its volume, which is associated with the manufacture of ribosomes.
NUCLEOTIDE	A monomer of nucleic acids consisting of a base, 5-carbon sugar and phosphate grouping.
NUCLEUS	A double membrane-bound organelle in cell cytoplasm which contains the genetic complement of the cell.

O

OBLIGATE PARASITE	An organism that cannot survive on its own; it must always live in or on another organism.
OIL	A lipid that is liquid at room temperature.
OPERATOR	The region of the chromosome in some organisms such as bacteria to which a repressor molecule may become attached, effectively preventing the synthesis of a protein such as an enzyme.
OPERON	A cluster of genes in some organisms such as bacteria that regulates the synthesis of a protein such as an enzyme.
OPPORTUNISTIC INFECTION	An infection that exploits some weakening of a host's normal resistance to that agent. For example, if the host is undergoing a course of immunosuppressive drugs after a transplant, he or she may be susceptible to bacterial or viral infection which normally would be prevented by the immune system.

KEYWORD	DEFINITION
ORGANELLE	A subcellular component that carries out a specific role, for example a mitochondrion.
ORGANOCHLORINE	A carbon compound that also contains chlorine. The basis of insecticides such as DDT.
OSMORECEPTOR	A specialized group of cells that can detect changes in the water concentration of the blood and respond by producing antidiuretic hormone; it is located in the hypothalamus of the brain.
OSMOREGULATION	Control of the water content and dissolved substances in the body fluids of animals.
OSMOSIS	Movement of water from an area of high water concentration to an area of low concentration across a selectively permeable membrane.
OUTBREEDING	This occurs when mating between close relatives does not take place, increasing the chance of hybrid vigour.
OVARY	The organ where the female sex cells are produced in plants and animals.
OVULE	The female gamete found in plants.
OVUM	The female gamete found in animals.
OXIDATION	The addition of oxygen.
OXIDATIVE PHOSPHORYLATION	The process of making adenosine triphosphate (ATP) which requires oxygen to be present.
OXYGEN DEBT	A state produced after vigorous exercise, where the demand for oxygen by skeletal muscles cannot be fully met by the normal process of breathing and so the body reverts to a modified form of respiration which is anaerobic. This produces lactic acid and a feeling of muscular fatigue. To recover from this, extra oxygen is required, delivered by panting, to repay the oxygen debt.

P

PALISADE MESOPHYLL	The layers of photosynthetic cells between the upper and lower epidermis which are tall and columnar shaped so that many of them can be packed close together. They possess many chloroplasts.

KEYWORD	DEFINITION
PANCREAS	An organ associated with the digestive tract, producing important enzymes such as trypsin and amylase, which are released into the duodenum. The pancreas also contains cells, in the Islets of Langerhans, which can secrete hormones such as insulin and glucagon, involved in the regulation of blood glucose levels.
PARAMECIUM	A one-celled animal that possesses hair-like structures called cilia on its body surface.
PARAQUAT	A synthetic weedkiller that is very toxic to humans.
PARASITE	An organism that lives on or in a host and is dependent on the host for nutrition and protection but causing damage to the host.
PARENCHYMA	Thin-walled packing cells that can take on a variety of structures and functions.
PARTHENOCARPY	The formation of a fruit without fertilisation so that seeds are absent.
PASSIVE IMMUNITY	Immunity associated with receiving ready-made antibodies to a particular antigen. This can be through artificial agents such as an injection or naturally in the mother's milk or through placenta.
PASSIVE TRANSPORT	Simple diffusion down a concentration gradient which does not require energy.
PATHOGEN	An agent such as a virus or bacterium that is capable of producing disease.
PECKING ORDER	The order of dominance in a group of mammals or birds. The most dominant animal gets first choice of resources such as food, space and mate.
PENTADACTYL	Having five fingers or toes such as is commonly found in amphibia, mammals, reptiles and birds.
PEPTIDE	Two or more amino acids joined together.
PEPTIDE BOND	The chemical bond formed between amino acids that results in the loss of a water molecule.
PERISTALSIS	Involuntary muscular contractions that propel materials along tubes such as the oesophagus or ureter.
PERSISTENCE	This describes a chemical that will not break down easily by natural means and may remain in the environment for a long time.

KEYWORD	DEFINITION
PERMEABLE	This describes a membrane that allows substances such as water to pass across easily.
PESTICIDE	A chemical used to kill pests which may be animal or plant in nature.
PHAGOCYTOSIS	The act of ingesting and digesting an antigen such as a bacterium by a cell of the immune system.
PHENOTYPE	The expression of the genes possessed by an individual. Such expression is usually a combination of the effects of the genes and the environment. Phenotypes need not be visible to the eye, for example blood groupings.
PHENYLKETONURIA	An inherited error of metabolism where a person lacks an enzyme so that an amino acid called phenylalanine accumulates in the blood, with some excreted in the urine. Excess phenylalanine in the blood causes brain damage in developing babies. Phenylketonuria is caused by a recessive allele. Abbreviated to PKU.
PHLOEM	A plant structure whose role is to move food material made in the leaves by photosynthesis to other parts of the plant.
PHOSPHATE	A chemical grouping consisting of phosphorus and oxygen.
PHOSPHOLIPID	A fat molecule that has two fatty acids, a phosphate group and a glycerol unit. Phospholipids are important components of cell membranes and responsible for many of the membrane properties.
PHOSPHORYLATION	The addition of a phosphate group to a molecule.
PHOTOLYSIS	The splitting of a water molecule during the light-dependent stage of photosynthesis.
PHOTOPERIOD	The length of daylight compared with the length of darkness over 24 hours.
PHOTOPHOSPHORYLATION	The formation of adenosine triphosphate in a process that requires light.
PHOTOSYNTHESIS	The process by which green plants use the energy of the sun to combine carbon dioxide and water to form carbohydrate. The green pigment chlorophyll is necessary for this process.
PHOTOTROPISM	The movement of a plant which is a growth response towards or away from light.

KEYWORD	DEFINITION
PHYTOALEXINS	A chemical produced by some plants after they have been damaged. It has antifungal and antibacterial properties.
PHYTOPLANKTON	Tiny plants found in the upper layers of oceans, lakes etc.
PIGMENT	A coloured compound produced by a living cell.
PINOCYTOSIS	The energy-demanding uptake of very small quantities of fluids by cells involving the formation of membrane-bound sacs at the cell surface. Alternatively known as 'cell drinking'.
PIONEER COMMUNITY	The plants that first colonize and survive in a new area of the environment.
PIT	In plants, a very small indentation or gap which is not bounded by a cell wall. Small strands of cytoplasm can communicate with other cells through such spaces.
PITUITARY	An important endocrine gland found in the base of the brain which secretes many hormones that orchestrate the activities of other endocrine glands such as the thyroid and sex organs, as well as directly influencing body processes.
PLACENTA	An organ formed from the developing embryo which forms a link with tissue from the mother. It allows exchange of gases and materials via their respective bloodstreams, and also has a hormone-secreting function.
PLACENTAL MAMMAL	Mammals such as humans that have a placenta.
PLASMA	The straw-coloured liquid part of the blood in which the cells are suspended.
PLASMA MEMBRANE	The boundary surface of a cell that acts as an interface between the cell contents and the external environment. Generally considered to be built on a fluid-mosaic model.
PLASMID	A small, circular piece of deoxyribonucleic acid (DNA) commonly found in bacterial cells and some other organisms such as yeasts. Bacterial plasmids often contain genes that give the bacterium resistance to certain antibiotics.
PLASMOLYSIS	The shrinking of a plant cell membrane away from the cell wall as a result of water loss.
PLASTID	A subcellular structure that is bounded by two membranes found in plant cells. Usually plastids contain pigments.

KEYWORD	DEFINITION
PLEUROCOCCUS	A one-celled plant often found growing on the bark of trees.
POINT MUTATION	Another name for a gene mutation.
POLIOMYELITIS	A viral infection that usually affects children and young adults, often causing paralysis.
POLLEN	The structure in a flowering plant that contains the male gamete.
POLYPEPTIDE	A relatively long sequence of amino acids joined by peptide bonds.
POLYPLOIDY	Possessing three or more sets of chromosomes per cell, whereas the usual number is two sets of chromosomes per cell. Polyploid plants are important in agriculture, because they often have increased growth potential compared with the normal variety.
POLYSACCHARIDE	A relatively long sequence of simple sugars that form important carbohydrates such as glycogen and starch.
POPULATION	A group of living things that belong to the same species and live in the same area of the environment.
POPULATION DENSITY	The number of individuals of any one species that live in a defined area of the environment.
POPULATION PYRAMID	A graphical way of displaying the numbers in a population with respect to their age and sex.
POROSITY	A measure of the ratio of volume of air spaces found within soil to the volume of soil particles. Highly porous soils will drain rapidly.
POSTERIOR	Located at the back of the body or at the back of an organ.
POTOMETER	Apparatus used to demonstrate the rate of transpiration in a plant by using a shoot.
PRECIPITATION	The general term for the release of water from the atmosphere in the form of rain, snow, dew etc.
PRIMARY CONSUMER	The first animal link in a food chain involving plant eaters; sometimes called a herbivore.
PRIMARY GROWTH	The growth of shoots and roots that tends to cause the plant to grow taller.
PRIMARY PHLOEM	Phloem produced during the early stages of growth of a plant.

KEYWORD	DEFINITION
PRIMARY RESPONSE	The initial reaction of the immune system to invasion by an antigen that is met for the first time. Usually it is relatively slow.
PRIMARY SUCCESSION	The sequence of plant growth, starting with bare ground.
PRIMARY XYLEM	Xylem produced during the early stages of growth of a plant.
PRIMATE	A mammal that has a placenta, nails, thumbs and big toes, including monkeys, apes and humans.
PRODUCER	A green plant at the start of a food chain which photosynthesizes to make its own food.
PROLACTIN	A pituitary hormone that stimulates the production of breast milk after the birth of a baby.
PROTEASE	The general name for any enzyme that can break down protein substrates.
PROTEIN	A very large polymer of amino acids joined together by peptide bonds.
PROTEIN PUMP	A protein molecule that acts as a carrier in the cell membrane to actively transfer molecules across.
PUNNETT SQUARE	A simple table devised by Ralph Punnett to show graphically all possible results from a genetic cross.
PUS	A viscous, yellow-coloured fluid formed at an infection site. Usually it contains dead white blood cells that have phagocytosed bacteria as well as some living bacteria and dead host cells.
PYRAMID OF BIOMASS	A graphical representation of the mass of living things measured at each feeding level in an ecosystem. Almost all ecosystems have greatest mass at base where the producers are found and least at the top where the carnivores are located.
PYRUVIC ACID	An important 3-carbon molecule that is an intermediary in the biochemical process of respiration. Pyruvic acid is formed from glucose in glycolysis.

R

RABIES	A viral infection that affects the brain of animals. Usually it enters at the site of a bite by an animal such as a dog or a bat.

KEYWORD	DEFINITION
RADIATION	The emission of energy in the form of waves or particles.
RECEPTOR	A specialised group of cells that can detect changes in an animal or plant body or in the environment.
RECEPTOR SITE	A molecule or group of molecules in a cell membrane adapted to fit another complementary molecule such as a hormone or an enzyme. When the two molecules link up, a change in cell function is usually brought about.
RECESSIVE ALLELE	An allele whose expression requires the presence of another, similar recessive allele on the other member of the homologous chromosome pair. Recessive alleles therefore require the individual to be homozygous for the recessive phenotype to develop.
RECOMBINANT	An organism that has a combination of genetic material different from either parent.
RECOMBINANT DNA TECHNOLOGY	The deliberate manipulation by humans of deoxyribonucleic acid (DNA) which has been altered in some way, for example by having genes removed or added.
RECOMBINATION	Mixing genetic material so that the resulting gene combination is different from the parental forms. Linked genes that cross over produce recombinations of the genes on those chromosomes.
RED BLOOD CELL	The more common name for an erythrocyte, a red blood cell that has no nucleus and contains haemoglobin. Its function is oxygen transportation.
REDUCING SUGAR	Any sugar which can be oxidized and is capable of reducing alkaline copper solutions such as Fehling's or Benedict's reagents.
REDUCTION	The loss of oxygen or the gain of hydrogen atoms.
REFLECTED LIGHT	Light that is not absorbed but is sent back towards the source.
REGENERATION	The replacement of body parts that have become damaged or lost. Regeneration is limited for the most part to lower animals.
REGULATORY GENE	A gene that codes for a protein repressor which in turn controls the activities of other genes.
REJECTION	The destruction of a transplant from another organism by the immune system.

KEYWORD	DEFINITION
REPLICATION	The production of an identical copy of a strand of deoxyribonucleic acid (DNA) which occurs during both mitosis and meiosis.
REPRESSOR	A protein that inhibits the function of the operator gene by binding to it.
REPRODUCTIVE BARRIER	The means by which a species becomes divided into two or more sub-groups because they are incompatible in some way or the offspring produced are not fertile.
RESAZURIN DYE	A chemical whose colour changes from blue to colourless and can be used to detect reducing activity.
RESIN	A high molecular weight substance secreted by some plants in response to wounding. Resins often harden to a glass-like substance, sealing the damaged area against fungal and/or bacterial invasion.
RESISTANCE	The random possession of a combination of mutations which gives an animal or plant immunity to some toxic agent. For example, some plants may have a genetic immunity to a particular weedkiller so that if applied it will artificially select those plants out to survive while killing all the others.
RESPIRATION	A biochemical process by which energy-rich substrate molecules are progressively enzymatically broken down to form adenosine triphosphate (ATP). Respiration usually takes place in the presence of oxygen (aerobic respiration) but can, to a limited extent, occur in its absence (anaerobic respiration).
RESPIROMETER	The apparatus used to monitor the rate of respiration of living things.
RESPONSE	Any reaction to a stimulus.
RETROVIRUS	A virus whose nucleic core is made of single-stranded ribonucleic acid (RNA) – and which can transfer this into a deoxyribonucleic acid (DNA)-containing host cell.
REVERSED STOMATAL RHYTHM	An adaptation shown by plants such as cacti that enables them to open their stomata during the evening rather than during the day. This helps prevent excessive water loss during the day.
REVERSE TRANSCRIPTASE	A special enzyme that can convert ribonucleic acid (RNA) into deoxyribonucleic acid (DNA) found in retroviruses.

KEYWORD	DEFINITION
RHIZOME	A stem that grows horizontally below ground level. It can grow leaves and roots.
RIBONUCLEIC ACID	A type of nucleic acid, abbreviated RNA. Two of these are very important in protein synthesis, messenger (mRNA) and transfer ribonucleic acid (tRNA). RNA is a large linear molecule that uses the bases adenine, uracil, cytosine and guanine in its construction.
RIBOSE	A 5-carbon sugar which is a component of RNA.
RIBOSOME	A sub-cellular, non-membrane-bound particle that is the site of protein synthesis.
RIBULOSE BIPHOSPHATE	A 5-carbon sugar that combines with carbon dioxide in the light-independent stage of photosynthesis to form two molecules of the 3-carbon molecule glycerate phosphate.
RICKETS	A deficiency disease caused by lack of vitamin D characterised by the lack of formation of healthy bones.
RNA POLYMERASE	An important enzyme in the transcription of deoxyribonucleic acid (DNA) into ribonucleic acid (RNA). One of the DNA strands acts as the template and the RNA polymerase joins nucleotides together to form the complementary RNA molecule.
ROAN	Of an animal, having white hairs mixed with a colour such as black or red.
ROOT HAIR	A cell found in the root of a plant which has a very large surface area for absorbing water and dissolved solutes.
ROOT NODULE	A small swelling on the roots of some plants, most notably those of the legumes such as peas and beans. These nodules contain bacteria that are capable of fixing atmospheric nitrogen and converting it into a form the plant can use as a nutrient.
ROOTING POWDER	A synthetic product that mimics the effect of natural growth hormones, such as auxins, in plants.
ROOT PRESSURE	The positive pressure formed in roots when the rate of transpiration is low. It tends to force water up the xylem vessels. The mechanism is thought to involve an active uptake of solutes into the xylem which then pulls water in by osmosis.

KEYWORD	DEFINITION
ROUGH ENDOPLASMIC RETICULUM	A series of interconnected flat membranes that are continuous with the nuclear membrane and covered with ribosomes. Associated with protein synthesis for export from the cell.

S

KEYWORD	DEFINITION
SEA LEVEL	A reference point for measuring relative heights of areas of land etc.
SECOND FILIAL GENERATION	Resultant offspring from a cross using two members of the first filial generation.
SECONDARY CONSUMER	An animal in a food chain which feeds on a herbivore.
SECONDARY GROWTH	Growth that causes the plant root and stem to growth outwards thus increasing the thickness. It is due mainly to the activity of laterial meristems such as cambium.
SECONDARY PHLOEM	Phloem formed during the secondary growth of a plant.
SECONDARY RESPONSE	A rapid reaction by the immune system to an antigen that has been previously encountered.
SECONDARY SUCCESSION	Plant succession that does not start on bare ground but on ground which has had growth previously that may have been interrupted in some way, for example by a fire.
SECONDARY THICKENING	The formation of new plant cells outwards as a result of the activity of cambium tissue which causes the plant to widen. The growth can then be seen as annual rings.
SECONDARY XYLEM	Xylem formed during the secondary growth of a plant.
SECRETION	The manufacture and passage across the cell membrane of useful chemicals such as hormones, enzymes and neurotransmitters.
SELECTIVE BREEDING	Artificially choosing animals and plants that have some desirable qualities and breeding only from them. A widely used technique to produce flowers of a particular colour or animals with a high milk yield etc.
SELECTIVE PERMEABILITY	The property of a cell membrane by which it can exert control on substances that pass across it.
SELECTIVE WEEDKILLER	A chemical that can be applied to a variety of plants but which will kill only a particular type. For example, selective weedkillers may be used on a lawn to render it weed-free without harming the grass itself.

KEYWORD	DEFINITION
SELF-POLLINATION	The transfer of pollen from the male part of one flower to the female part of the same flower or onto another flower on the same plant.
SEMI-CONSERVATIVE REPLICATION	The method by which a dexoyribonucleic acid (DNA) molecule makes a copy of itself such that the two new identically formed strands each contain half of the original (parent) DNA molecule.
SENESCENCE	The process of ageing in animals and plants.
SESSILE	A term normally used to describe an animal or plant which does not move.
SET POINT	The value for some variable (such as temperature, blood glucose level) which, if departed from, sets in motion a corrective mechanism to reduce the change.
SEWAGE	The collective name for human urine and faeces that are taken via sewers and drains for treatment and conversion into a safer form.
SEX CELL	A gamete or haploid reproductive cell such as a sperm or ovum.
SEX CHROMOSOME	A chromosome that determines the sex of an individual. For example, in humans, males have XY, while females have XX.
SEX-LINKED GENES	Genes that are located on one of the sex chromosomes. In most animals, it is usually the X chromosome that carries these.
SEX-LINKED INHERITANCE	A pattern of inheritance in which the genes concerned are located on the sex chromosomes; most commonly associated with the X chromosome. Well-known examples include haemophilia and colour blindness.
SEXUAL REPRODUCTION	A reproductive process that involves the manufacture of two different types of sex cells which then fuse to form a new individual whose genetic makeup is different from either parent.
SHADE-TOLERANT PLANT	A plant such as the *Begonia* that can grow well in low light intensity.
SHORT-DAY PLANT	A plant that requires a short light period in order for it to flower. Chrysanthemum and strawberry are short-day plants.

KEYWORD	DEFINITION
SHRUB	A low-growing, woody plant that does not have a main trunk to its body. Usually a shrub does not grow much above 6 m in height.
SICKLE-CELL ANAEMIA	An inherited disease that affects the red blood cells. Causes a sickle shape of the red blood cell to develop through an abnormally formed haemoglobin molecule (HbS sickle-cell haemoglobin). Single gene is involved and this is located on chromosome number 11 with two allelic forms.
SIEVE CELL	A long, slender cell, with no nucleus, that forms the sieve tube, and each ends in a sieve plate.
SIEVE PLATE	A series of holes that are found at the end of a sieve cell. Cytoplasm, in the form of strands, connects sieve cells next to each other through these holes.
SIEVE TUBE	A series of sieve cells that lie end to end to form a hollow canal.
SIGMOID CURVE	An S-shaped curve that might be found, for example, in the growth pattern of humans.
SMOLT	A young salmon.
SMOOTH ENDOPLASMIC RETICULUM	A series of interconnected flat membranes that are continuous with the nuclear membrane and not covered with ribosomes.
SMOOTH MUSCLE	Muscle that forms the gut and the walls of blood vessels, the uterus etc. It is not under conscious control and so is sometimes called involuntary muscle.
SOCIAL GROUP	A collection of individuals who share the same types of behaviour patterns, attitudes etc.
SOCIAL SIGNAL	A stimulus given out by an animal to communicate with other animals of the same species. May include threat behaviour and sounds.
SOMATIC CELL	Any cell of the body other than a sex cell.
SOMATIC FUSION	The technique of causing two cells, often from different species, to merge and produce one new single cell which possesses the combined features of each of the parent cells.
SOMATOTROPHIN	Another name for growth hormone.
SPECIATION	The formation of two or more groups of organisms that can no longer interbreed to form fertile offspring.

KEYWORD	DEFINITION
SPECIES	A group of individuals which can interbreed to form fertile offspring.
SPECIFIC IMMUNITY	A defence that is targeted at a particular antigen and usually involves the production of a specific antibody.
SPECTROPHOTOMETER	An instrument that can detect the intensity of particular wavelengths of light in a spectrum.
SPECTRUM	An arrangement of light according to its wavelengths.
SPELT	An ancient, commercially unimportant type of wheat, grown in parts of Europe, that modern wheat species were developed from.
SPERM	A male sex cell that contains half the normal number of chromosomes and determines sex.
SPINDLE	A network of fibres that appear during meiosis and mitosis. The spindle attaches to chromosomes at their centromeres and moves them to opposite poles of the cell.
SPONGY MESOPHYLL	A layer of irregularly shaped cells found between the upper and lower epidermis that create a large surface area and many air spaces within the leaf.
STALKED PARTICLE	Structures revealed under an electron microscope, located on the cristae of mitochondria; they are the site of the production of adenosine triphosphate (ATP) in aerobic respiration.
STARCH	A polysaccharide made up of many monomers of glucose. It is the principle storage carbohydrate of plants and widely found in human food.
STEM CELL	A cell which is capable of growing into many different types of cell found in the adult animal or plant.
STICKY END	The end of a deoxyribonucleic molecule where one strand continues beyond the other by a few bases. Two sticky ends can join together if the bases are complementary to each other.
STIMULUS	An energy event in the environment or within a plant or animal body which can be detected by a receptor and potentially produces some kind of response.
STOMA	A small pore on the surface of leaves and stems that allows exchange of materials between the environment and the plant. Plural is stomata.

KEYWORD	DEFINITION
STROMA	The colourless material within the chloroplast where the light-independent stage of photosynthesis takes place.
STRUCTURAL GENE	A gene that codes for an enzyme or other essential protein necessary for the cell to function.
STRUCTURAL PROTEIN	A long chain of amino acids that is used as part of the fabric of the cell such as part of the membrane.
STUBBLE	The remains of a reaped field such as straw.
SUBSISTENCE FARMING	An agricultural practice in which the land will yield just enough to support the farmer, leaving little or nothing to be sold for profit.
SUBSTITUTION	A mutation in which a base in the deoxyribonucleic acid (DNA) molecule is replaced by another one so that there is no net gain or loss in the number of bases.
SUBSTRATE	A chemical on which an enzyme acts. Usually there is a one-to-one relationship between an enzyme and its substrate.
SUCCESSION	The changes that occur with the passing of time in the numbers and composition of plants in a given area from its initial colonisation.
SUCCULENT TISSUE	Tissue that is fleshy and filled with a lot of water. Found for example in desert-dwelling plants whose stems have become swollen with water.
SUCKLING	The act of an animal drawing milk from its mother's breasts.
SURFACE AREA TO VOLUME RATIO	The measure of the relationship between the surface area of an animal or plant body and its volume.
SYNDROME	A combination of symptoms that may in themselves seem unrelated but which can be used to identify a specific condition such as Down's syndrome.

T

TANNIN	One of a group of complex chemicals found in plant leaves, unripe fruit etc. They have a most unpleasant taste which may function to discourage herbivores from eating these plants.

KEYWORD	DEFINITION
TAR	A highly toxic group of chemicals found in cigarette smoke and potentially cancer-causing. Tar contains a complex mixture of hydrocarbons, oils etc.
TARGET CELL	Any cell that will respond to a particular hormone or chemical messenger.
TEMPLATE	With reference to nucleic acids, one strand of the deoxyribonucleic acid (DNA) molecule, which can act as a pattern against which a new complementary DNA strand can be synthesised or a complementary strand of ribonucleic acid (RNA) formed.
TENDON	A tough, fibrous protein structure connecting muscle to bone. Tendons are inelastic, allowing the force of muscle contraction to be transmitted to bone, and consist of parallel fibres made of collagen.
TERRITORY	A specific area in the environment that is inhabited by one species which will not allow members of the same species to share it; often associated with the breeding season and defended by the resident animal.
TESTA	The tough coat that protects a seed.
TEST CROSS	A cross where one parent is homozygous recessive for the particular gene being checked. A test cross is used to determine an unknown genotype.
TESTIS	An organ in the male animal where sperm are produced, usually in very large numbers.
THALIDOMIDE	A drug once used as a cure for morning sickness in pregnant women. It can pass across the placenta, causing severe foetal abnormalities such as loss of limb.
THERMORECEPTOR	A group of specialized nerve cells that can detect heat or cold and are widely found throughout the skin.
THERMOSTAT	A device that will maintain a pre-set temperature, often used as an analogy for the heat-control centre found in the hypothalamus.
THYMINE	One of the five bases that form nucleotides of nucleic acids.
THYROID	A hormone-producing gland found in vertebrate animals, usually situated in the base of the neck region. It produces the hormone thyroxine.

KEYWORD	DEFINITION
TRANSPIRATION	The evaporative loss of water through the aerial surfaces of a land plant.
TRANSPLANT	Tissue or an organ from a donor which is to be placed into a recipient host.
TRIAL-AND-ERROR LEARNING	A random change in an animal's behaviour that has come about by the association of a stimulus, with either a desirable or undesirable outcome of some kind.
TRIOSE PHOSPHATE	A 3-carbon sugar containing a phosphate group.
TRIPLET CODE	Based on a grouping of three nucleotides in ribonucleic acid (RNA) or deoxyribonucleic acid (DNA) which determines one amino acid.
TRUE-BREEDING	A genotype that is homozygous for a particular gene or group of genes. The offspring normally will not show any variation of the phenotype if both parents are similarly homozygous.
TULLGREN FUNNEL	Apparatus used to extract animals from soil or leaf litter etc.
TURGIDITY	The state of a plant cell that is full of water.
TURNER'S SYNDROME	A chromosomal mutation affecting females in which the individual has 45 chromosomes instead of 46; one X-chromosome is missing. Turner's syndrome causes a female phenotype but with some of the secondary sexual features not fully developed; such females are infertile.

U

UNICELL	An organism such as the *Amoeba* that consists of only one cell.
UNLEARNED BEHAVIOUR	Behaviour which is a result of the genetic make-up and does not need to be learned by experience. Also known as innate behaviour.
URACIL	One of the five bases that form nucleotides of nucleic acids.
UREA	A nitrogen-containing substance formed in the liver from excess amino acids and then excreted in the urine.
URINE	A fluid excreted by the kidneys which is mainly water with various dissolved solutes such as urea, ammonia, salts and trimethylamine oxide.

KEYWORD	DEFINITION
V	
VACCINATION	The deliberate, artificial exposure to a modified antigen to provoke the immune system into conferring immunity without inducing the disease itself.
VACCINE	The modified form of an antigen that will provoke the immune system into producing antibodies but which will not cause the disease itself, only mild symptoms or none at all. A vaccine can be in the form of weakened forms of live bacteria, modified poisons etc.
VALVE	A structure that allows movement of contents of a tube or blood in the heart to flow in one direction only.
VARIABLE	A quantity that can continually increase or decrease such as temperature and pH.
VARIATION	A difference that exists between living things which may be a function of the genotypes or the environment or both.
VASCULAR BUNDLE	A strand of the tissue that forms pathways which run up and down the stems and roots of advanced plants. A vascular bundle contains xylem and phloem separated by cambium.
VASOCONSTRICTION	A narrowing of the arteries as a result of the contraction of the muscles found in their walls so that the flow of blood is severely reduced.
VASODILATION	A widening of the arteries as a result of relaxation of the muscles found in their walls so that the flow of blood is enhanced.
VECTOR	In genetics this is a piece of deoxyribonucleic acid (DNA) that carries a gene to be inserted into another organism. Viruses and plasmids may be used as vectors.
VEGETATIVE REPRODUCTION	In plants this is an alternative name for asexual reproduction.
VEIN	A vessel carrying blood away from the heart.
VERTEBRA	One of 33 small bones in humans, which, stacked on top of each other, form the vertebral column (backbone).
VESICLE	A membrane-bound sac found in cell cytoplasm.
VESSEL	Any tube which has well-defined walls and can carry liquids such as blood or dissolved sugars.

KEYWORD	DEFINITION
VESTIGIAL	Having little or no function, for example the appendix in humans.
VIRUS	A sub-cellular parasite that can only exist in a living cell.
VITAMIN	Any of the chemicals that are required, usually in small amounts, for normal health. Usually referred to by letters, as in vitamin A, vitamin C etc.

W

KEYWORD	DEFINITION
WAGGLE DANCE	A system of communication used by honeybees to convey to other members of the group where and how far a food source is.
WALL PRESSURE	The pressure exerted on the plant cell wall by the contents of the vacuole pressing against it, giving the plant support.
WATER CYCLE	The natural circulation of water through an environment where water is lost to the atmosphere by evaporation and rises to form clouds that later condense to cause the water to be deposited on land as snow, rain etc.
WATER TABLE	The level below which all spaces are filled with water.
WEED	A plant growing in an undesired location.
WEIL'S DISEASE	A bacterial infection of dogs, rats and other mammals that can be transmitted to humans. It causes severe fever, headache etc.
WHITE BLOOD CELL	The common name for a leucocyte.
WHITE LIGHT	Light containing all the possible wavelengths within the visible range.
WINDBREAK	Anything that will protect against the force of the wind such as a fence or line of trees.

X

KEYWORD	DEFINITION
XANTHOPHYLL	One of a group of accessory yellow or brown pigments used in photosynthesis.
XEROPHYTE	A plant that thrives in an environment where the water availability is very limited.

KEYWORD	DEFINITION
XYLEM	A group of plant cells that transports water and dissolved solutes from the roots to the leaves.
Y	
YEAST	A general term for a fungus that exists as a unicell. Some yeasts can be used to ferment sugar to alcohol.
Z	
ZYGOTE	A fertilized egg at the one-cell stage which contains a full genetic complement of chromosomes.